THE TOP TEN
POP
SONGS
EVERY **BEGINNER**
PIANIST
SHOULD **LEARN**

WISE PUBLICATIONS
part of The Music Sales Group
London / New York / Paris / Sydney / Copenhagen / Berlin / Madrid / Hong Kong / Tokyo

Published by
Wise Publications
14-15 Berners Street,
London W1T 3LJ, UK.

Exclusive Distributors:
Music Sales Limited
Distribution Centre, Newmarket Road,
Bury St Edmunds, Suffolk IP33 3YB, UK.
Music Sales Corporation
180 Madison Avenue, 24th Floor,
New York NY 10016, USA.
Music Sales Pty Limited
Level 4, Lisgar House,
30-32 Carrington Street,
Sydney, NSW 2000 Australia.

Order No. AM1012297
ISBN 978-1-78558-404-6

Notes written by Sandy Burnett.

Photographs courtesy of:
Page 6 – Paul Natkin/WireImage
Page 14 – Getty Images
Page 24 – Chris Walter/WireImage
Page 30 – Theo Wargo/Getty Images
Page 38 – Michael Putland/Getty Images
Page 44 – Michael Ochs Archives/Getty Images
Page 54 – Carlos Alvarez/Getty Images
Page 60 – Matthew Baker/WireImage
Page 66 – John Rogers/Getty Images

Every effort has been made to trace the copyright holders
of the photographs in this book but one or two were unreachable.
We would be greatful if the photographers concerned would contact us.

Printed in the EU.

THE TOP TEN POP SONGS EVERY BEGINNER PIANIST SHOULD LEARN

Why did you start to learn the piano? Many people are inspired by seeing an awesome artist perform on this expressive and versatile instrument, or they are desperate to play a particular piano-based song they love. Whatever the motivation, there's always a bit of a journey from non-musician to virtuoso, and you may not find 'Mary Had A Little Lamb' and other much-loathed beginner tunes the most enthralling pieces to play. But if you want to play pop, how do you know which pieces are suitable for a new player?

That's where we come in. The music industry has churned out millions and millions of songs over the years, so we've curated some of the most famous and accessible tunes that are suitable for beginners and satisfying to play. We've hand-picked both old-school and modern classics from over 50 years of pop greatness, covering a range of styles and artists from Nina Simone to Coldplay and Bill Withers to Adele. So if you want to learn a few tunes to impress your friends, or just for the sheer love of it, we're confident this little collection will give you just what you're looking for.

CHASING CARS

ARTIST: Snow Patrol
RELEASED: 2006

Snow Patrol did pretty well with their 2003 album *Final Straw* – it reached number three in the charts and produced four top 40 singles in the UK. But they did even better with *Eyes Open*, which sold four million copies worldwide after its release in 2006. All of which came as bit of a surprise to the band, who had been in the business and trying to break through since 1994, the year when three young students met at Dundee University and began to follow their rock dream. As Snow Patrol's Gary Lightbody wryly put it, 'We were a 10-year overnight success.'

But the real success story of their *Eyes Open* album was the hit single that came from it. 'Chasing Cars' stayed in the UK charts for some 85 weeks; it was reckoned to have been the most widely-played song in the UK in the first decade of the millennium – quite something – while further afield, music lovers right across the world got to know it after the track was featured in the second season of the popular TV series *Grey's Anatomy*. In fact, if you were looking for a song to sum up the sound of the noughties, this would have to be a strong contender.

CHASING CARS

Words & Music by Paul Wilson, Gary Lightbody,
Jonathan Quinn, Nathan Connolly & Tom Simpson

1.
A5
2.
A5
A
For-get what we're told
be-fore we get
E/G♯
4fr
A5/D
too old.
Show me a gar - den that's
A
burst-ing in-to life.

Let's waste time chas - ing cars a - round our heads. I need your grace to re - mind me to find my own. If I lay

am, all that I ev - er was___

is here in your per - fect___ eyes,___ they're all I can see.___

I don't know where,

con-fused a - bout how as well,___ just know that these

12

things   will nev - er   change___ for   us at all.___   If   I   lay

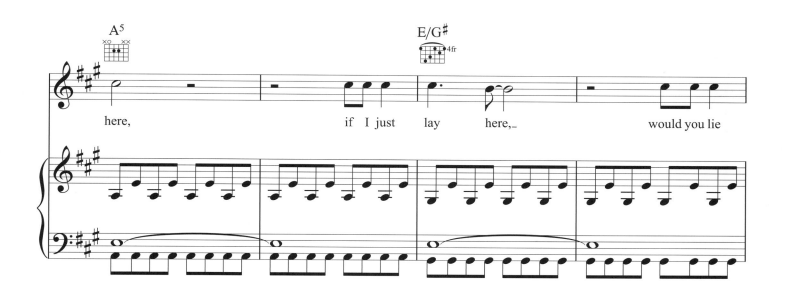

here,   if   I just   lay   here,_   would you lie

with   me___ and_   just for - get the world?___

FEELING GOOD

ARTIST: Nina Simone
RELEASED: 1965

One of the real originals of twentieth-century popular music, Nina Simone owes her distinctive sound to the depth of her musical origins. Firstly, there was the church, a dominant guiding force in the North Carolina community she was born into in 1933. Then there was her early introduction to the world of classical music – Bach, Beethoven, Schubert and Brahms – via an English piano teacher by the name of Muriel Mazzanovich (Miss Mazzy, as Nina called her), who had moved to the area. Finally, there was all that time spent re-interpreting the classics of the Great American Songbook by singing them in bars and night clubs, a move which never quite won the approval of her mother, who used to refer to it as 'working in the fires of hell.'

Nina Simone's version of the Newley/Bricusse song 'Feeling Good' comes from her 1965 album *I Put A Spell On You*. Those references in the lyrics to 'a new dawn, a new day, a new life…' allowed her to do what she did best – offer a spiritual insight into our daily lives. And that's something that Michael Bublé picked up on in his later 2005 version, which has become, for twenty-first-century audiences, every bit as much of a success.

FEELING GOOD

Words & Music by Leslie Bricusse & Anthony Newley

Birds fly-in' high, you know how I feel._ Sun in the sky,___ you know how I feel.___

Breeze_ drift- in' on by,___ you know how I feel.___ It's a

new dawn, it's a new day, it's a new life___ for___ me, yeah. It's a

new dawn,___ it's a new day,____ it's a new life for me.___

Ooh,_____ ooh,_____ and I'm feel - in' good.___

18

Dra - gon - fly out in the sun,__ you know

what I mean,__ don't you know? But - ter - flies all hav - in' fun,_____

you know what I mean. Sleep in peace when day_____ is

ma na na na na na ma na da ya da da   mm ma dah-mm mah___   ma. Oh, I'm feel - in'

good.

23

HE AIN'T HEAVY, HE'S MY BROTHER

ARTIST: The Hollies
RELEASED: 1969

One of the most powerful pop ballads of the late 60s, 'He Ain't Heavy, He's My Brother' was written by two Americans, Bobby Scott and Bob Russell, and was first recorded over there by Kelly Gordon. How the British pop group The Hollies got to hear about it was down to a stroke of luck; their guitarist and vocalist Tony Hicks spotted the sheet music for the song lying on a publisher's desk in London.

As another member of The Hollies, Allan Clarke, remembers: 'We thought that maybe ballads weren't our thing at that time, but the actual message of that song got through to us. We thought that we've got to give this song a chance.' The powerful image of carrying a brother down a long road with many a winding turn was too much for The Hollies to resist, and so they went into the famous Abbey Road studios in the summer of 1969 and committed their version to disc. It's not only The Hollies on that record, though; playing piano that day was a certain young session musician from Pinner in Middlesex. Elton John was his name – I wonder what happened to him?

HE AIN'T HEAVY, HE'S MY BROTHER

Words & Music by Bob Russell & Robert William Scott

26

HELLO

ARTIST: Adele
RELEASED: 2015

When you think about it, 'Hello, it's me' is a pretty good way of opening an album. And for Adele, making a return to the public consciousness with her album *25*, it was an approach that just felt right for her. Following on from her debut album *19* and the massive success of her follow-up record *21*, *25* is the third album that Adele has named after her age. It's a process that she compares to taking photographs of her life, which had moved on aplenty since album number two, most significantly because of the birth of her son.

If *21* was a break-up record, *25* switched things round to reflect on making up. Written with her producer Greg Kurstin, the song turns the spotlight not on how other people have made Adele feel, but on how she has made herself feel. There's darkness in 'Hello' for sure, right from the start with that descending F minor groove, but there's plenty of positivity and feelings of empowerment too. It's turned out to be yet another Adele success story, chalking up a record-breaking million downloads in a week, and reaching number one in almost every single country it was released in.

HELLO

Words & Music by Greg Kurstin & Adele Adkins

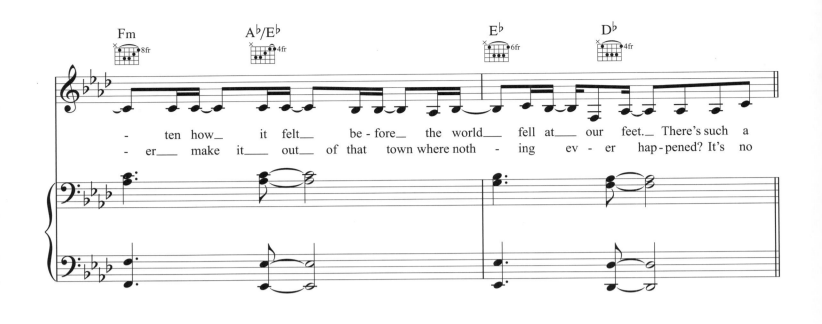

- ten how_ it felt_ be - fore_ the world_ fell at_ our feet._ There's such a
- er_ make it_ out_ of that town where noth - ing ev - er hap - pened? It's no

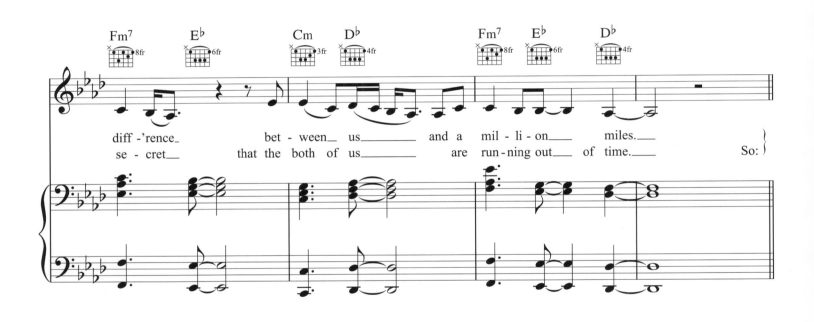

diff - 'rence_ bet - ween_ us_ and a mil - li - on_ miles._
se - cret_ that the both of us_ are run - ning out_ of time._ So:

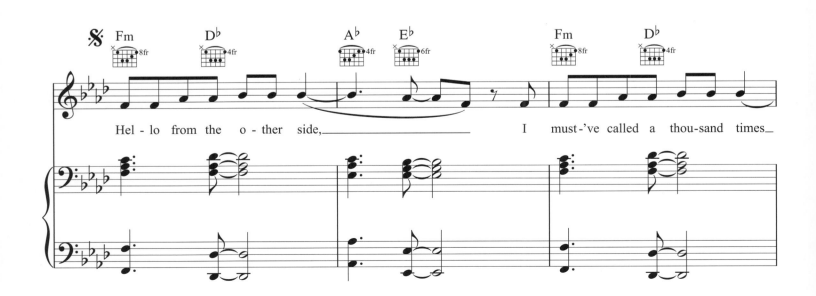

Hel - lo from the o - ther side,_____ I must -'ve called a thou - sand times_

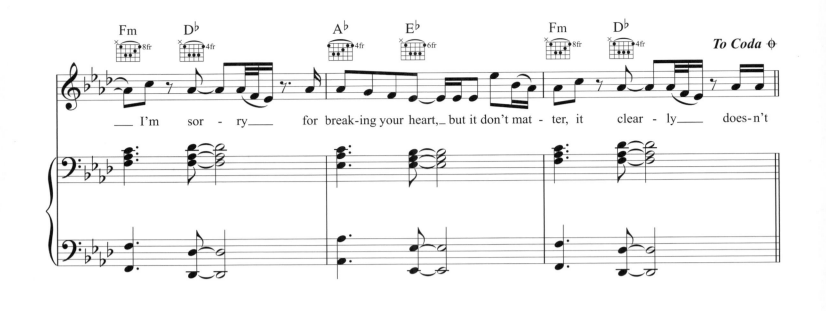

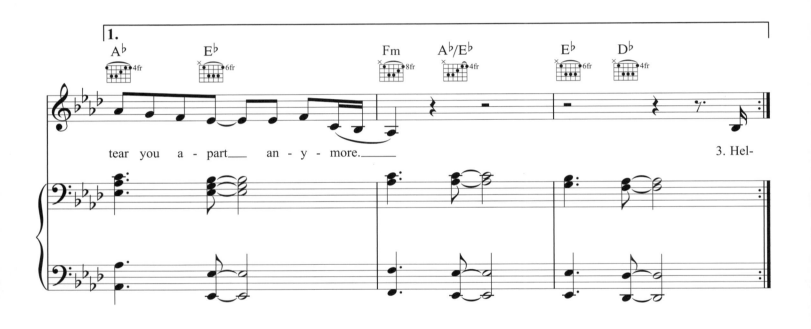

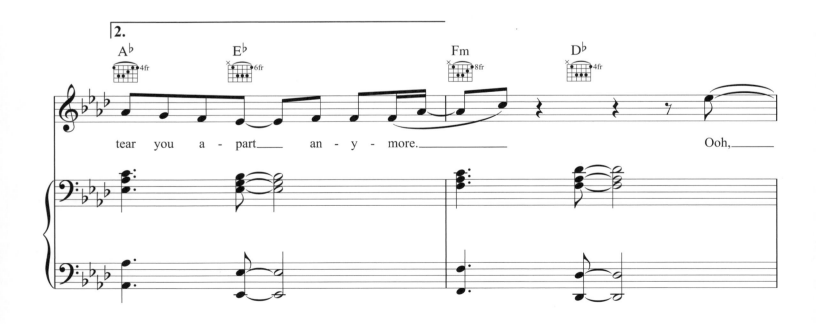

37

KINGSTON TOWN

ARTIST: UB40
RELEASED: 1990

'Kingston Town' was a hit for the first time in 1970 for its composer with the splendid stage name of Lord Creator, and then for the second time in 1990 over in the United Kingdom, when the song was dusted off by a certain band from Birmingham. Their members came from many different ethnic backgrounds – from English, Irish, Jamaican, Scottish and Yemeni parentage. In their early days, they had one significant thing in common: they were all unemployed. In fact, they took their band name from the form that you needed to fill in to claim unemployment benefits back in those days: UB40.

Over the years, UB40 have sold some seventy million records, making them one of the most successful bands in the world. What's driven them from the outset is a love for the kind of reggae music that the band members had grown up with and wanted to make their own. As the liner notes to UB40's earlier 1983 album *Labour Of Love* put it, reggae was a style of music that 'appealed not to the intellect or the social conscience, but to the heart and hips.'

KINGSTON TOWN

Words & Music by Kenrick R. Patrick

there are won - ders_____ for ev - 'ry -
there is mag - ic_____ in

- one._____ (Woah.)_____ 2. The King -

- ston Town._____ Oh,

King - - ston Town,_____ the place I

43

LEAN ON ME

ARTIST: Bill Withers

RELEASED: 1972

Famous for his warm and grainy voice on songs such as 'Lovely Day' and 'Just The Two Of Us', Bill Withers has made an indelible contribution to popular music. But it's one he delivered on his own terms; after breaking through in 1970 and recording and performing through until 1985, he then stepped aside from his music career altogether, leaving a clutch of major hits as memories.

Bill puts the success of his music down to the fact that he worked hard to say things in the simplest possible terms. 'Lean On Me', which was a massive hit for him in 1972, is a case in point. It's not just the directness of the lyrics, and the message of not being afraid of asking for, or offering, help – values he grew up with in his hard-working West Virginia childhood – there's the structure of his music too. Bill wrote the song soon after he'd made enough money from music to buy a Wurlitzer electric piano for the first time. Through playing the instrument in the simplest possible way, letting his fingers run up and down the keys, the stepwise contours of the opening phrase of 'Lean On Me' came into being, just like that.

LEAN ON ME

Words & Music by Bill Withers

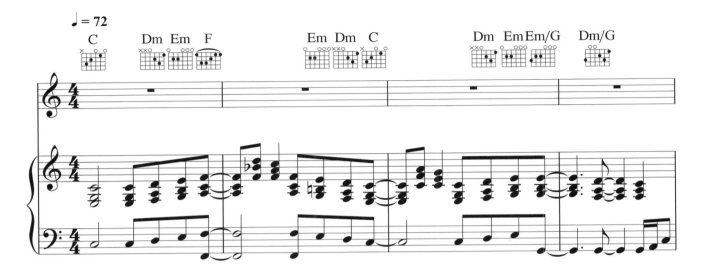

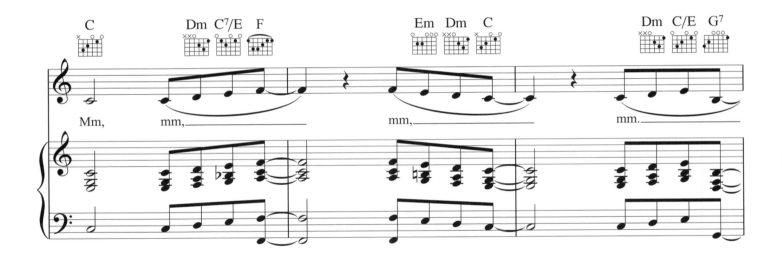

Mm, __ mm, _____ mm, _____ mm.

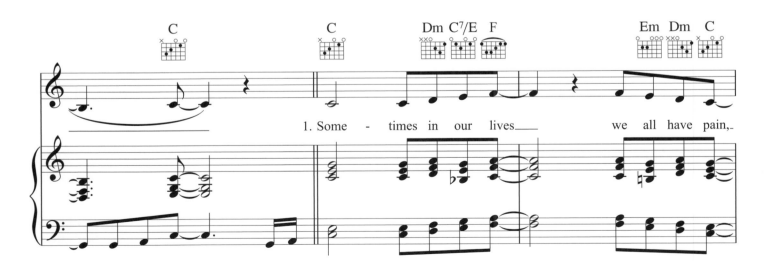

1. Some - times in our lives ___ we all have pain, __

47

MAD WORLD

ARTIST: Michael Andrews feat. Gary Jules
RELEASED: 2001

This song first cropped up in the early eighties – 'Mad World' was one of the big early hits for Tears for Fears, eminent synth-pop band that rode the wave of, well, the New Wave in those trailblazing days for British music. With its driving drums and swirling synthesiser sounds, 'Mad World' made it to number three in the UK charts late in 1982.

Then again, you might know the tune from *Donnie Darko*, which came out two decades later. A dark psychological film that is tricky to sum up in a single sentence, it stars Jake Gyllenhaal as an emotionally disturbed teenager from suburban Virginia who gets night-time visits from a six-foot rabbit… Anyway, 'Mad World' appears in the film's end sequence, as reworked by the film's composer Michael Andrews – he asked his vocalist friend Gary Jules to come up with some additional lyrics, which he duly did. In their hands, not only did the song make it into the charts for a second time, it became the UK's Christmas number one in 2003. 'Mad World' mark two is quite a different take on the first, with simple but moody piano chords underpinning a plaintive vocal, and that's the version we're presenting here.

MAD WORLD

Words & Music by Roland Orzabal

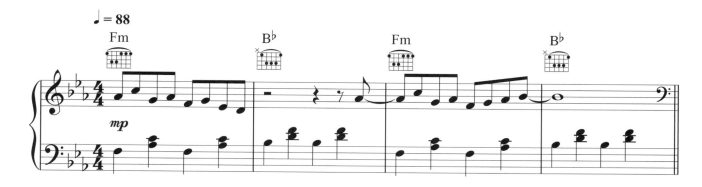

1. All a-round me are fa-mi-liar fa- ces, worn out pla - ces,
2. Chil-dren wait-ing for the day they feel__ good, hap-py birth - day,

*2° only till ***

worn out fa - ces._____ Bright and ear-ly for their dai-ly ra-ces,
hap-py birth-day._____ And I feel the way that ev-'ry child__ should,

SHE'S THE ONE

ARTIST: Robbie Williams
RELEASED: 1998

A moody groove on two simple chords introduces one of the most recorded pop songs of the past few years. 'She's The One' was initially written by Karl Wallinger for the British rock band World Party, and it got him an Ivor Novello award in 1997 before being picked up and performed by all sorts of star vocalists from Andy Williams to Olly Murs. The standout version in the minds of most, though, is the one Robbie Williams made in 1999. Taken as the second single from his album *I've Been Expecting You*, Robbie's rendition sold close to half a million copies in the UK, released as a double A-side along with 'It's Only Us'. With its soaring vocal lines, it's not a million miles away from 'Angels', a power ballad that Robbie had had a big hit with a couple of years previously. The song has become a firm favourite on TV's *The X Factor* ever since Robbie duetted with One Direction on the track in the 2010 series. Whether he sings it solo or in company, it's really thanks to him that 'She's The One' has become one of the most well-known love songs of our time.

SHE'S THE ONE

Words & Music by Karl Wallinger

If there's some-bod - y   call - ing me on,__
If there's some-bod - y   call - ing me on,__

she's the one.__
she's the one.__   2. We were young,__

we were wrong,_____   we were fine_____   all a-long._____   If there's some-bod -

- y   call - ing me on,_____   she's the one.__

STAY WITH ME

ARTIST: Sam Smith
RELEASED: 2014

Sam Smith's love of singing goes way back. Being overheard in the car at the tender age of eight led to lessons that saw him tackling everything from jazz to the musicals. Later came the long, hard slog to success, which saw his voice featured on singles by Disclosure and Naughty Boy, and then the enormous interest generated by *In The Lonely Hour*, his debut solo album that led to him selling out huge live venues in a matter of minutes.

For all the years of prep, 'Stay With Me', the third single from *In The Lonely Hour*, actually fell into place pretty quickly: just half an hour or so, according to Sam, who remembers getting together with collaborators Jimmy Napes and William Phillips in a studio in London's Old Street. First came three chords on the piano, then a drum pattern, and after that, 'the song just flowed out of us so naturally.'

STAY WITH ME

Words & Music by Tom Petty, Jeff Lynne,
James Napier, Sam Smith & William Phillips

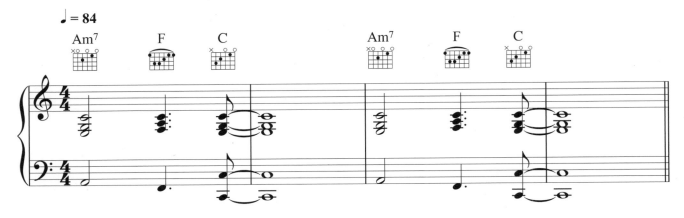

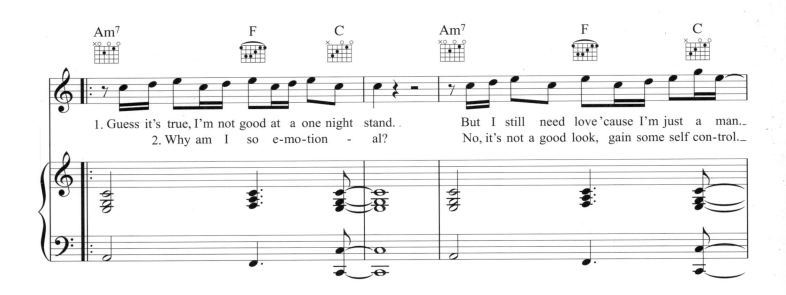

1. Guess it's true, I'm not good at a one night stand. But I still need love 'cause I'm just a man.
2. Why am I so e-mo-tion-al? No, it's not a good look, gain some self con-trol.

These nights nev-er seem to go to plan.
And deep down I know this nev-er works.

I don't want you to leave, will you hold my hand?
But you can lay with me so it does-n't hurt.

Oh, won't you

stay____ with me?____ 'Cause you're_ all____ I need.__

To Coda

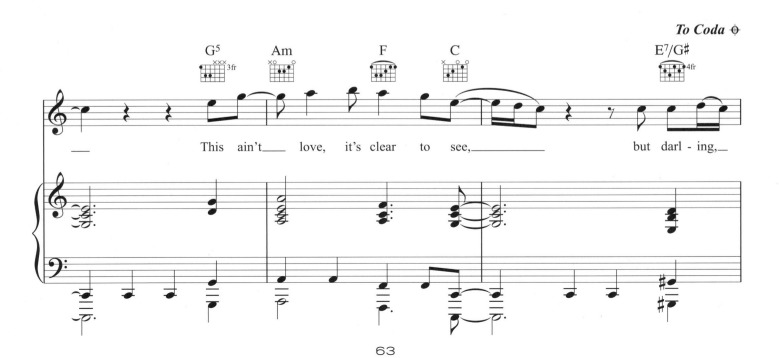

This ain't___ love, it's clear to see,_____ but darl-ing,__

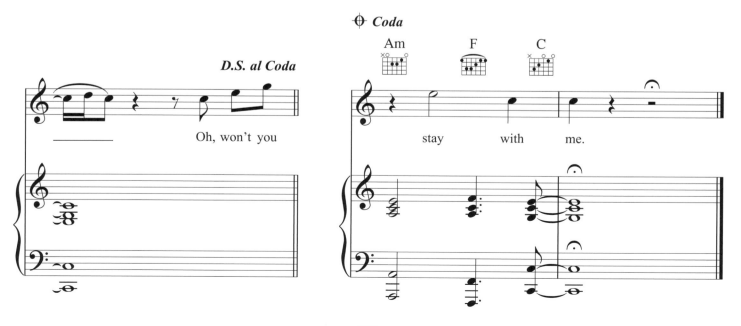

THE SCIENTIST

ARTIST: Coldplay
RELEASED: 2002

One night not long after the millennium, the lead singer of Coldplay, Chris Martin, sat down at an out-of-tune piano in Liverpool. He'd set out to work on a song by the late great George Harrison, but things took quite a different turn. Chris found himself creating a sequence of four chords which had a circular feel about them, with no definite sense of where or when the sequence would stop. Lyrics followed swiftly, and the essence of the song, the voice part and piano track, was recorded then and there. It was one of the last tracks to make it onto

Coldplay's *A Rush Of Blood To The Head*, and the song was released late in 2002 as the second single from the album. Its title 'The Scientist' is said to refer to Dan Keeling, the record company executive who signed Coldplay to Parlophone; the third verse has a reference to 'guessing at numbers and figures, pulling the puzzles apart.' But the main thrust of the song discusses the difficulties of love, which are far more complicated to resolve than any scientific problem could ever be. As the song puts it, 'Nobody said it was easy…'.

THE SCIENTIST

Words & Music by Guy Berryman, Chris Martin,
Jon Buckland & Will Champion

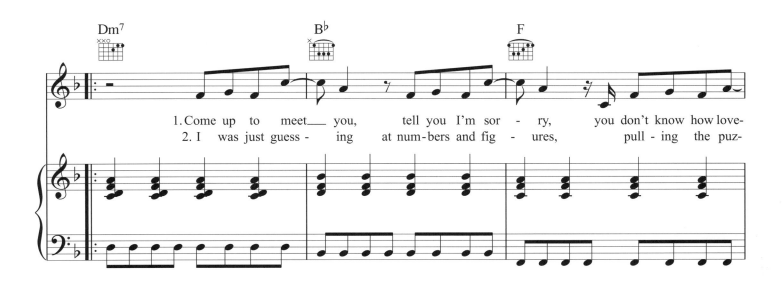

1. Come up to meet____ you, tell you I'm sor - ry, you don't know how love-
2. I was just guess - ing at num - bers and fig - ures, pull - ing the puz-

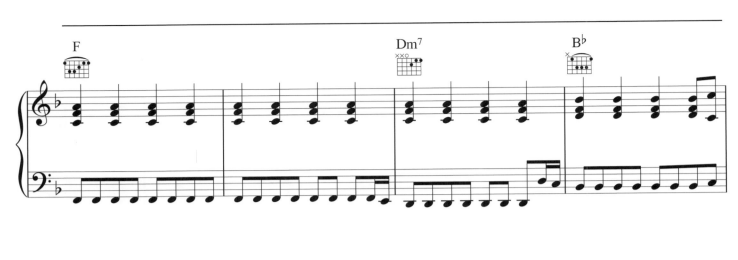

THE TOP TEN...

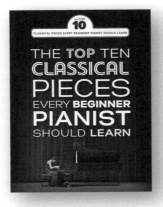

THE **TOP** TEN
CLASSICAL PIECES
EVERY BEGINNER
PIANIST
SHOULD LEARN
AM1012231

THE **TOP** TEN
MOST BEAUTIFUL
PIECES TO PLAY
ON PIANO
AM1012253

THE **TOP** TEN
CHRISTMAS
SONGS TO PLAY
ON PIANO
AM1012484

THE **TOP** TEN
LOVE SONGS
TO PLAY
ON PIANO
AM1012275

THE **TOP** TEN
PIANO SONGS
OF ALL TIME
AM1012242

THE **TOP** TEN
CONTEMPORARY
CLASSICAL PIECES
TO PLAY ON PIANO
AM1012286

THE **TOP** TEN
MOST CALMING
PIECES TO PLAY
ON PIANO
AM1012319

THE **TOP** TEN
FILM THEMES TO
PLAY ON PIANO
AM1012264

THE **TOP** TEN
POP SONGS EVERY
BEGINNER PIANIST
SHOULD LEARN
AM1012297

THE **TOP** TEN
JAZZ SONGS TO
PLAY ON PIANO
AM1012308